I SPY
SCHOOL DAYS

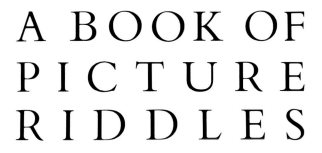

A BOOK OF
PICTURE
RIDDLES

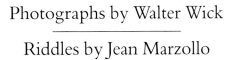

Photographs by Walter Wick

Riddles by Jean Marzollo

Hippo

For my nieces, Heather, Jessica and Emily,
and my nephews, David, Peter and Michael

———————

W.W.

For Marjorie Holderman, Joanne Marien and Gerrie Paige

———————

J.M.

Also available in the I SPY series:

I SPY: A BOOK OF PICTURE RIDDLES

I SPY CHRISTMAS: A BOOK OF PICTURE RIDDLES

I SPY MYSTERY: A BOOK OF PICTURE RIDDLES

Book design by Carol Devine Carson

Scholastic Children's Books,
Commonwealth House, 1–19 New Oxford Street, London WC1A 1NU
A division of Scholastic Ltd
London ~ New York ~ Toronto ~ Sydney ~ Auckland

First published by Scholastic Inc, 1995
This edition published by Scholastic Ltd, 1996

Textcopyright © Jean Marzollo, 1995
Photographs copyright © Walter Wick, 1995

Hardback ISBN 0 590 54283 4
Paperback ISBN 0 590 19160 8

Typeset by Rapid Reprographics
Printed in Singapore

10 9 8 7 6 5 4 3 2

The rights of Jean Marzollo and Walter Wick to be identified as the author
and photographer of this work respectively has been asserted
by them in accordance with the Copyright, Designs and Patents Act, 1988

TABLE OF CONTENTS

Picture riddles fill this book;
Turn the pages! Take a look!

Use your mind, use your eye;
Read the riddles—play I SPY!

I spy a magnet, a monkey, a mouse,
A pumpkin, two flags, five 4's, a house;

A spinning top, a watering can,
A UFO and a yellow van.

I spy a rabbit, a rhyming snake,
An apple, a shark and a birthday cake;

An unfinished word, a whale, a can,
A dog, a cat and a small blue man.

I spy an acorn, a daisy, a 3,
A shell in a nest, a shell from the sea;

Three feathers, two frogs, a ladybird too,
Ten drops of water, and thread that is blue.

I spy a frog, a draughtboard 3,
A zigzag 4, and a green palm tree.

A rabbit, an arrow, a girl named DOT,
Six red blocks, and the missing knot.

I spy a marble, a clothes peg clamp,

FUN, two keys, and a ruler ramp;

Three helmets, a hand, a hammer, a heart,
A magnet, a chair, and a blackboard chart.

I spy a school, three camels, a bell,
A lighthouse, a swan, and a basket that fell;

A paintbrush, a drum, an upside-down block,
A calendar card, and a grandfather clock.

I spy a post van, a valentine cart,
A blue eyeball I, and a five-button heart;

Six arrows, two horses, two planes, two clocks,
A key, and a card that is in the wrong box.

I spy a chimney, an anthill, a four,
A face with a smile, a star, and a score;

A feather, a twig, three footprints, a key,
A boat, two birds, a button, and BE.

The Stegosaurus ate plants for food.
Bobby C.

Stegosaurus walks on four legs and is my favorite dinosaur.
Rosa

Nobody knows what they are really like because they only have the bones.

This shows how big a stegosaurus is compared to a school bus.
Jee...

Stegosaurus brain was only as big as a walnut.

Stegosaurus' tail spikes could

I spy a walnut, two turtles, a pail,
Two eggs that are hatching, a clothes peg, a snail;

Ten pine cones, an ant, a shovel, a plane,
A little red star, three frogs, and a chain.

I spy a bike, three ladders, and CLOCKS,
A small piece of chalk, four half-circle blocks;

A limo, a phone, and a rolling pin,
A flame, eight stars, and DEW DROP INN.

I spy three carrots, a magical hen,
Four keys, a candle, a cat, and a ten;

A teapot, a tin man, a rabbit asleep,
Anansi the Spider, and Little Bo Peep.

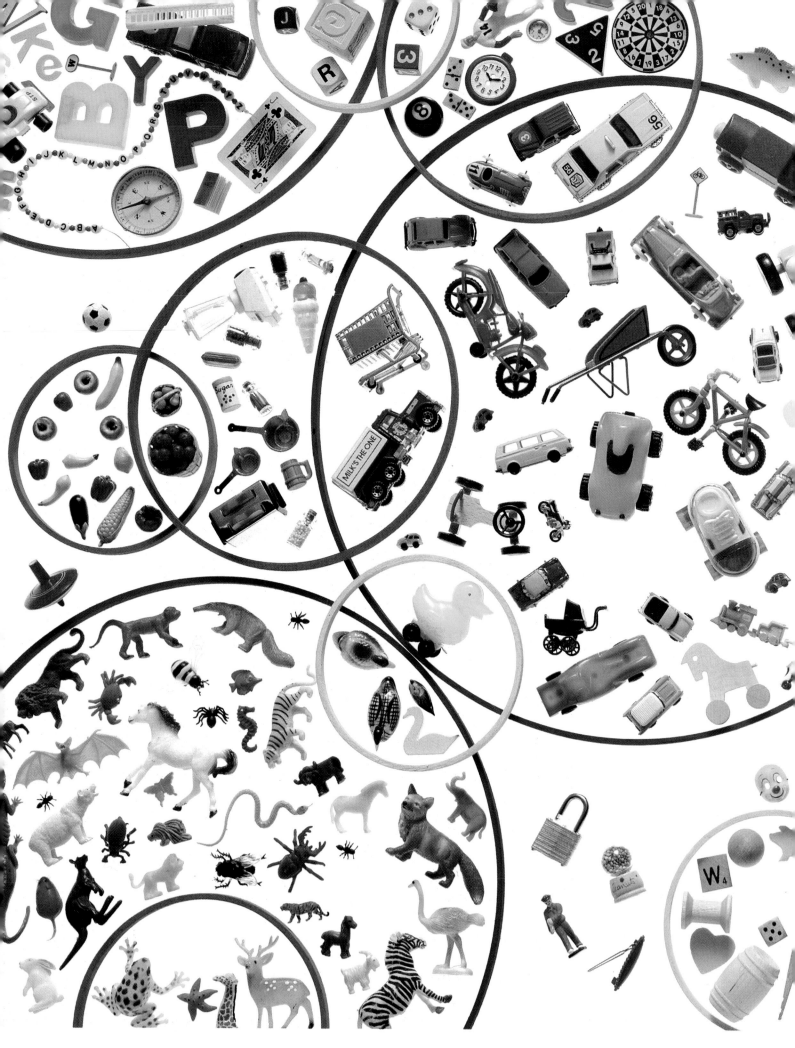

I spy a padlock, an ostrich, a bat,
A pig, three ants and a man with a hat;

An alphabet necklace and five yellow rings,
And places for all of the outside things.

I spy a spider, an ice skate, a rake,
Two bracelets that match, a trumpet, a cake;

A fan, the Big Dipper, three flowerpots,
A coat with four buttons, and ten paper dots.

EXTRA CREDIT RIDDLES

"Find Me" Riddle

I'm yellow; I buzz. If you look, you will see.

I'm in every picture. I'm a busy little _____.

Find the pictures that go with these riddles:

I spy a ruler, a hanger, a wrench,

Eight traffic cones, and an empty bench.

I spy Rapunzel, a small piece of cheese,

A boy in a well, and two glitter keys.

I spy a starfish, a paper-clip chain,

A cow, seven hearts, and a yellow jet plane.

I spy a school bus, a camel, a lamp,

Two question marks, and a postage stamp.

I spy a sea horse, a spotted cow,

Three butterflies, and the cat's MEOW.

I spy scissors and three striped cats,

Three pen points, and two yellow hats.

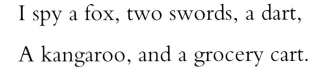

I spy a penny, a leaf that's turned red,

Two black ants, and a grey arrowhead.

I spy a fox, two swords, a dart,

A kangaroo, and a grocery cart.

I spy a feather and two equal signs,

A piece of pie, and three dotted lines.

I spy a truck, a shovel, a J,

Eight rubber bands, and some orange clay.

I spy a shovel, two rabbits, a yak,

A coin, a knight, and a purple jack.

I spy a starfish, a capital I,

A pencil, a snake, and a dragonfly.

I spy a car and a speckled stone,

A chain, a seed, and a small pine cone.

Write Your Own Picture Riddles

There are many more hidden objects and many more possibilities for riddles in this book. Write some rhyming picture riddles yourself, then try them out with your friends

Walter Wick, the inventor of many photographic games for *Games* magazine, is the photographer of the *I Spy* books. He is also a freelance photographer. Mr Wick graduated from the Paier Art School in New Haven, Connecticut. This is his sixth book for Scholastic.

Jean Marzollo, a graduate of the Harvard Graduate School of Education, has written many children's books including the *I Spy* books.

Acknowledgements

Again, we are grateful for the support and assistance of Grace Maccarone, Bernette Ford, Edie Weinberg, and many others at Scholastic. We also very much appreciate the help of Molly Friedrich at Aaron Priest Agency, Linda Cheverton-Wick, Elizabeth Woodson, Tiny Chaden, Barbara Ardizone, Maria McGowan, Bruce Morozko, Frank and Ray Hills, Denis Gouey, Gator Laplante and Lee Hitt. To Kevin Williams we extend a special thanks for his valuable and patient assistance throughout the entire *I Spy School Days* project.

Walter Wick and Jean Marzollo

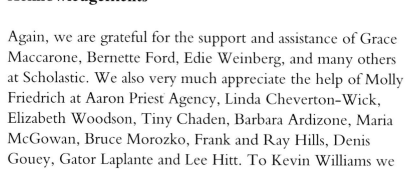